MY EASY-TO-READ STORIES

ILLUSTRATED BY PAMELA STOREY

STORIES BY JUNE WOODMAN

BRIMAX BOOKS · NEWMARKET · ENGLAND

Here is a collection of amusing animal stories with a very simple repetitive text primarily designed for children of 4–7 years who are ready to read.
The text is presented in large type.
In addition to each story is a special section to encourage the revision of new words and concepts to stimulate observation and memory.
Children will love the easy-to-read stories of Dilly Duck, Paddy Dog, Hoppy Rabbit, Bossy Bear, Cuddly Cat, Flippy Frog and their friends.

ISBN 0 86112 353 0
© BRIMAX BOOKS LTD 1986. All rights reserved.
These stories also appear as individual books.
Published by BRIMAX BOOKS, Newmarket, England 1986
Second printing 1987
Printed in Hong Kong

Contents

SILLY
DILLY DUCK

Dilly Duck goes to the pond.
Her three little ducklings
go with her.
"Come with me," says Dilly.
"I will take you for a swim
in the duck pond."
But the little ducklings are
afraid. They do not want
to go to the duck pond.
"We do not know how to
swim!" they say.
But Dilly Duck does not
hear them.
Silly Dilly Duck!

Bossy Bear plays with
his roller-skates. He has
a lot of fun.
He sees Dilly Duck come
along the lane. He sees
the three little ducklings
with her.
"Where are you going?"
says Bossy Bear.
"To the duck pond," says the
first little duckling.
"But I do not want to go."

"Why not?" says Bossy Bear.
"I cannot swim," says
the first little duckling.
"We can play a trick," says
Bossy Bear.
"I will go to the duck pond.
You stay here. You can play
with my roller-skates."
The first little duckling
thinks that will be fun.
He puts on the skates.

Dilly Duck is on her way to
have a swim in the duck pond.
The two little ducklings
and Bossy Bear go along too.
But silly Dilly Duck does not
see Bossy Bear.
The two little ducklings and
Bossy Bear think that this
is very funny. Bossy Bear
likes to play funny tricks.

They all go along the lane.
Soon they meet Hoppy Rabbit.
He drives in his little car.
"Where are you going?"
says Hoppy Rabbit.
"To the duck pond," says
the second little duckling.
"But I do not want to go."
"Why not?" says Hoppy.
"I cannot swim," says
the second little duckling.

Hoppy sees Bossy Bear.
"I am a duckling," says Bossy.
Hoppy thinks that this is very
funny.
"I will go to the duck pond
too," he says. "Duckling can
drive my car. This is
a very funny trick. Silly
Dilly Duck cannot see us."
The second little duckling
gets into Hoppy's car.

They all go along the lane.
Dilly Duck,
   Bossy Bear,
      Hoppy Rabbit
and one little duckling.
But Dilly Duck does not see
her very funny ducklings.

Soon they meet Paddy Dog.
Paddy Dog plays with his
little red scooter.
"Where are you going?"
says Paddy Dog.
"To the duck pond," says
the third little duckling.
"But I do not want to go."
"Why not?" says Paddy Dog.
"I cannot swim," says
the third little duckling.

Paddy Dog thinks that
this is very funny.
"Bossy and Hoppy are very
funny ducklings," he says.
"I will play a trick too.
Duckling can play with
my little red scooter.
I will be the third
little duckling. Silly
Dilly Duck will not see."

They all go along the lane.
Dilly Duck,
Bossy Bear,
Hoppy Rabbit
and Paddy Dog.
But no little ducklings!
Ozzie Owl is in the old tree.
"Hoo-hoo-hoo!" he hoots.
Cuddly Cat jumps down from
the tree. She thinks they
are all very funny.

29

At last they come to the pond.
Flippy Frog and Merry Mole
are there. They say,
"What funny ducklings."
Then Dilly Duck sees them.
She is afraid. She looks all
round for her lost ducklings.
And here they come!
One on skates,
one in the car,
one on the scooter.

But the little ducklings go
too fast. They cannot stop!
SPLASH! SPLASH! SPLASH!
Three little ducklings
fall into the pond.
Bossy Bear, Hoppy Rabbit
and Paddy Dog are all afraid.
"What can we do?
The three little ducklings
cannot swim," they say.

"You are silly!" says
Dilly Duck.
"You must know that all little
ducklings can swim."
She hops into the pond too.
Off they go.
Dilly Duck goes first and the
three little ducklings swim
behind her. Silly Dilly Duck
is not so silly after all!

Say these words again

thinks

afraid

first

jumps

duckling

swim

trick

plays

roller-skates

drives

second

funny

scooter

third

What are they doing?

skating

falling

jumping

driving

swimming

37

PADDY DOG
sees a GHOST

Paddy Dog is in his little house. It is a very windy day. Paddy looks out of the window. He sees the leaves falling off the trees.
"It is a good day for doing some washing," he says. Paddy Dog likes to be clean.

Paddy goes to get all his
dirty washing.
"My sheets are dirty," he says,
"and my pillow case too."
Paddy takes the table cloth.
He takes his scarf and his
dirty socks. He puts all the
dirty things into the wash tub.

Then Paddy Dog fills the wash
tub with very hot water.
He puts in lots of soap powder.
Then he rubs and he scrubs
until his things are clean.
Paddy goes outside to hang
the clean things on the line.
The wind is blowing hard.

"Now I will go and see Dilly
Duck," says Paddy Dog.
He goes to the duck pond.
Dilly is washing her three
little ducklings.
"It is a good day for doing
washing," says Paddy Dog.
"You are silly!" says Dilly.
"The wind is blowing too hard.
Look! All your washing is
blowing away."

"Oh no!" says Paddy Dog. He runs down the lane after his washing. He finds his socks in the hedge. He finds his table cloth on a bush. Flippy Frog finds the scarf and pillow case. They are in the pond.

Poor Paddy Dog.
His washing is all dirty.
He cannot find his sheet.
It is not in the hedge.
It is not in the bush.
It is not by the duck pond.
Is it in the forest?

It is very dark in the forest.
Paddy Dog is afraid.
Something goes "Hoo-hoo-hoo!"
Paddy sees something white.
It is up in the tree.
"A ghost!" says Paddy Dog.
He is not very brave.
Paddy Dog runs away fast.

Paddy runs to Hoppy Rabbit's
house. Hoppy is outside,
washing his little car.
He rubs and he scrubs until
it is clean.
"There is a ghost in the
forest!" says Paddy.
"No," says Hoppy Rabbit.
"Yes," says Paddy. "It is up
in the tree."
"Let us tell Bossy Bear,"
says Hoppy Rabbit.

They run to Bossy Bear's
house. Bossy is outside,
washing the windows.
He rubs and he scrubs until
they are clean.
"There is a ghost in the
forest!" say Hoppy and Paddy.
"No," says Bossy.
"Yes," say Hoppy and Paddy.
"It is up in the tree."
"Let us tell Dilly Duck,"
says Bossy.

57

Dilly and her ducklings are by the duck pond. Merry Mole and Flippy Frog are there too. "There is a ghost in the forest!" say Paddy and Hoppy and Bossy.
"You are silly!" says Dilly.
"Come and see," says Paddy Dog.

So they all go to the forest.
They are afraid, but they
try to be brave.
Then they see something
white in the tree.
"Hoo-hoo-hoo!" it goes.
They all hear it.
"It is a ghost!" says Dilly.
They are not brave at all.
They run away.

Then Cuddly Cat comes by.
She sees something white.
"Hoo-hoo-hoo!" it goes.
"What is that?" says Cuddly.
"It is a ghost in the tree,"
says Paddy Dog.
"I will go and see," says
Cuddly Cat.
"Look out!" says Hoppy.
"The ghost will get you!"

But Cuddly is very brave.
She goes up in the tree.
She lifts up part of the sheet.
"Hoo-hoo-hoo!"
"Look!" says Cuddly Cat.
They all shout,
"We know you!"
It is not a ghost.
It is Ozzie Owl!

Say these words again

windy	clean
blowing	shout
washing	pillow
window	soap powder
outside	something

What can you see?

tub

window

ghost

car

tree

HAPPY
HOPPY RABBIT

It is Hoppy Rabbit's birthday.
He puts out all the things
for his birthday party.
He finds a cloth to put
on the table. He puts the
food on the table too. There
are lots of good things
to eat.

All Hoppy's friends come
to the party. Paddy Dog and
Bossy Bear come first.
"Happy Birthday, Hoppy!"
they say.
"Here is a present for you,"
says Paddy. He gives Hoppy
a big red ball.
"Thank you," says Hoppy,
"I like to play games with
a ball."

Bossy Bear has a present for Hoppy too.
"Oh, look. It is a kite!"
says Hoppy.
"Look, here come Merry Mole and Flippy Frog," says Bossy.
"Happy Birthday, Hoppy," they say. Flippy gives Hoppy a big bunch of flowers.
"I like flowers," says Hoppy.

Merry Mole has some carrots
for Hoppy.
"I like eating carrots,"
he says. "Thank you."
Then Cuddly Cat comes with
a big basket.
"Thank you," says Hoppy.
He puts all his presents
into the basket.

Here comes Dilly Duck with
her three little ducklings.
She has made a birthday
cake for Hoppy.
The ducklings give him lots
and lots of big balloons.
Hoppy is very happy with
all his birthday presents.

"Time to eat!" says Hoppy.
They all go to the table
and they begin to eat.
They eat and they eat until
all the food is gone.
"I like birthdays," says
Hoppy. "Time to play some
games now."

They go outside to play with the big red ball. Hoppy throws it to Paddy. He throws it high into the air. The others try to catch it. They jump up high, but no one can get the ball. Then Cuddly Cat jumps up on to the fence. Now she can catch it.

"This is a very good game!" says Cuddly.

The wind begins to blow.
"Good!" says Hoppy. "Now
I can play with my kite."
He gets the red and blue kite
and he begins to run. The
wind is blowing hard, and
the kite goes up in the air.
"Look at it fly!" says
Bossy Bear.

"Let me have a go," says Paddy.
The kite goes up in the air.
"Let me have a go," says Dilly.
She begins to run, but she does not see Flippy Frog.
BUMP!
She falls over poor Flippy.
Silly Dilly Duck!

Dilly lets go of the kite and it goes up into the air. "Oh no!" they all say. Hoppy, Paddy and Bossy jump up to catch it. But it is stuck high up in the tree. They cannot get it.

Poor Hoppy Rabbit.
He is not very happy now.
"Look!" says Bossy. "I can
get it for you."
Bossy gets up into the tree.
He gets the kite and he begins
to come down.

Then Bossy stops.
"Oh no!" he says.
"I am stuck!"
Bossy cannot get down.
"What can we do?" says Dilly.
"Look!" says Hoppy. He runs
to get all the balloons.
Then he gets the basket.
He ties the balloons to the
basket. Then he lets it go.

Up goes the basket!
It goes up into the tree.
"Get in, Bossy!" says Hoppy.
So Bossy gets into the basket
and it begins to come down.
Down and down it comes.
BUMP!
The basket is down,
Bossy is down,
and the kite is down too!
"What a happy birthday!"
says happy Hoppy Rabbit.

Say these words again

cloth

friends

food

eat

first

present

games

outside

air

throws

catch

jumps

wind

stuck

What can you see?

flowers

carrots

balloons

kite

basket

BOSSY BEAR
at the CIRCUS

The circus is in town!
Bossy Bear loves the circus.
He runs to tell his friend,
Hoppy Rabbit.
"The circus is in town!"
says Bossy.
"I love the circus," says
Hoppy. "Come on,
we must go."
They get into Hoppy's car
and off they go.

They stop at Paddy Dog's
house. He is outside.
"The circus is in town!"
say Bossy and Hoppy.
"I love the circus," says
Paddy. "I want to go too."
"Hop into the car," says
Hoppy Rabbit.
Paddy gets into the car
and off they go.

They stop at the duck pond.
Dilly Duck and her three
ducklings are there with Merry
Mole and Flippy Frog.
"The circus is in town!" say
Bossy and Hoppy and Paddy.
"We love the circus. We want
to go too," say the three
little ducklings.
"Hop into the car," says
Hoppy Rabbit.
They all get into the car
and off they go.

Soon they get to the big
circus tent. They go inside.
Then the circus begins.
"Look, here come the lions!"
says Hoppy Rabbit.
The lions do lots of tricks.
"I can do tricks too," says
Bossy Bear. "Look at me!"
He runs into the circus ring.

But the lions are cross with
Bossy. They hit him with their
big paws and he falls down.
BUMP!
"Oh! Oh! Stop it!" says Bossy.
The lions roar at him and
Bossy Bear runs away.
"He is very funny," say Merry
Mole and Flippy Frog.
"He is very SILLY!" says
Dilly Duck.

"Here come the sea lions!"
says Paddy Dog.
The sea lions are very clever.
They do lots of tricks.
"I can do tricks too," says
Bossy Bear. "Look at me!"
He goes into the circus ring
with the sea lions. He takes
a big blue ball and puts it
on his nose.

But the sea lions are cross with Bossy. They want the blue ball back. They slap him with their flippers and throw wet fish at him.

"Oh! Oh! Stop it!" says Bossy. He runs out of the ring.

The sea lions move after him. "Bossy is funny," say Merry Mole and Flippy Frog.

"Look at the elephants!"
says Dilly to her ducklings.
The elephants go round the
circus ring. Each one holds
on to the next one's tail.
Last of all comes a little
baby elephant.
"I love the baby elephant,"
says Cuddly Cat.

Bossy runs into the ring
and pulls the tail of the
baby elephant.
"Look at me!" says Bossy
Bear.
But the baby elephant is
very cross. It slaps Bossy
with its trunk.
Bossy Bear falls down.
BUMP!
"Bossy is very funny," say
the three little ducklings.

"Look, here come the clowns!"
they all say. The clowns run
into the ring. They have
a bucket of water and a big
bucket of paste. They can do
very clever tricks. They do
not get wet. They do not
get sticky.
"I can do tricks too!"
says Bossy Bear.

"Come here, Bossy," say the
clowns. "Come and be the
new circus clown."
They give him a funny hat and
big black boots. Then they
give him a big red nose.
"Here is a funny new clown!"
they all say.
"Look at me!" says Bossy
Bear.

Bossy can do some tricks, but he is not so clever. His boots are much too big for him and he falls over.
BUMP!
He falls into the bucket of water. Then he falls into the bucket of paste.
Poor Bossy is very wet and very sticky.
But he does look funny!

"Stay and be a clown, Bossy,"
say the other clowns.
"Oh no, Bossy!" says Cuddly.
"Oh no, Bossy!" says Dilly.
Bossy is very wet and sticky.
He is very cross too.
"No!" says Bossy. "The circus
is no fun for a clown. I think
I will just be Bossy Bear!"

Say these words again

sticky
flippers
paws
roars
blue
throws
slaps

last
baby
tail
trunk
bucket
water
paste

What can you see?

elephant

circus tent

lion

clown

sea lion

WHERE IS CUDDLY CAT?

It is a very wet day.
The rain is coming down
very hard. Flippy Frog
comes hopping along down
the lane.
Plop! Plop! Plop!
"I like wet days," says
Flippy Frog. "It is never
too wet for me."

Flippy comes to Cuddly
Cat's little house.
He hops up to the window.
Plop! Plop! Plop!
When he looks inside,
Flippy sees a nurse.
She has a white cap with
a red cross on it. She has
a long white skirt.
"Where is Cuddly?" says
Flippy Frog.
He hops away very fast.

Soon Flippy comes to
Hoppy Rabbit's house.
Hoppy is busy mending his
gate.
"Help!" says Flippy. "There
is a nurse at Cuddly's house."
"Where is Cuddly?" says
Hoppy.
"She must be sick," says
Flippy. "We must help her."
So they hurry back to
Cuddly Cat's house.

They both look in at
Cuddly Cat's window.
"I see a nurse with a red
cross on her cap," says
Hoppy.
"I told you so," says
Flippy.
But where is Cuddly Cat?
"Stay here, Flippy," says
Hoppy. "Cuddly must be sick.
I will tell Paddy Dog."
He hops away down the lane
as fast as he can.

Paddy Dog is in his house.
He is mending his clock.
"There is a nurse in poor
Cuddly's house," says
Hoppy.
"She must be sick," says
Paddy Dog. "We must go
and help her."
They both hurry back and
look in at the window.

"I can see the nurse," says
Paddy Dog.
"I told you so," says Hoppy.
But Paddy can see someone
else.
"Look! I can see a doctor
too," he says.
"Oh, POOR Cuddly!" says
Hoppy. "She MUST be sick."
But where is Cuddly Cat?

"Stay here," says Paddy.
"I will go and tell Bossy
Bear."
He runs as fast as he can to
Bossy's house. Bossy is
mending his window.
"Cuddly Cat must be sick.
We can see a nurse and
a doctor in her house," says
Paddy Dog.
"Poor Cuddly," says Bossy.
"We must go and help her."

They run back and look into
Cuddly Cat's window.
"I can see the nurse and the
doctor," says Paddy Dog.
But Bossy Bear can see
someone else.
"Help!" he says. "I can
see a pirate there too.
The pirate has a black hat
and big black boots."

145

"What can we do?" says Paddy Dog.

"You stay here," says Bossy. "I will go and tell Merry Mole."

He runs off as fast as he can and soon he sees Merry Mole. Merry is busy digging a hole.

"Help!" says Bossy. "There is a nurse in Cuddly Cat's house. There is a doctor there and a pirate too."

They run back to the house.
They look in at the window.
"Poor Cuddly!" says Merry.
"I can see the nurse and
the doctor and the pirate."
"I told you so," says Bossy.
"And there is someone else.
I can see a funny clown,"
says Merry Mole.
But where is Cuddly Cat?

"What can we do?" says
Bossy Bear.
"You stay here," says Merry.
"I will go and tell Dilly
Duck."
He runs as fast as he can.
Dilly is coming down the
lane. Her three little
ducklings are with her.
"Help!" says Merry Mole.
"There is a nurse, a doctor,
a pirate and a clown. They
are all in Cuddly Cat's
house!"

"You are silly!" says Dilly.
"Come and see," says
Merry Mole.
So they all hurry to the house.
The three little ducklings
run to look in.
"We can see a nurse and
a doctor, a pirate and
a clown," they say.
"I told you so," says Merry.
"Look! There is a king too,"
say the little ducklings.
But . . .
WHERE IS CUDDLY CAT?

Then Dilly Duck looks in.
"You ARE silly!" says Dilly.
"Here is Cuddly Cat. Here
are Flippy, Hoppy, Paddy and
Bossy too. They are all
playing with Cuddly's
dressing-up box."
"Come in," says Cuddly Cat,
the nurse. "We can all play
dressing-up. It is a lovely
game for a wet day!"

Say these words again

plop

house

white

cross

black

pirate

stay

someone

mending

skirt

hurry

sick

doctor

poor

Who can you see?

a nurse

a king

a doctor

a clown

a pirate

FLIPPY FROG KEEPS FIT

It is a very hot day.
The sun is out and the
flowers are out. Flippy Frog
is out too. He likes to swim
in the pond on very hot days.
He jumps into the pond . . .
PLOP!
He swims off very fast.
Then Flippy begins to huff
and Flippy begins to puff.
"I am not fit," he says.

He swims to the other side of
the pond and hops out . . .
PLOP!
Then he hops off to look for
Dilly Duck. He hops along very
fast. But soon he begins to
huff and puff.
He sits down on the grass to
have a rest. The sun is hot
and Flippy Frog is hot too.
"I am not fit," he says.

Here comes Dilly Duck.
She runs after her three
little ducklings. She cannot
catch them. Dilly begins to
huff and puff.
"You are not fit, Dilly," says
Flippy Frog. "Come with me."
"Where are you going?" says
Dilly Duck.
"To the Keep Fit Class,"
says Flippy Frog.

Here comes Hoppy Rabbit.
His car will not go. Hoppy
begins to push it. But the
sun is hot and he huffs and
he puffs.
Bossy Bear comes by on his
roller-skates. He begins to
huff and puff too.
"You are NOT FIT!" says
Flippy Frog. "Come with us
to the Keep Fit Class."

"Look at Paddy Dog on his
scooter," say the three
little ducklings.
Paddy goes very fast, but
he huffs and puffs.
Cuddly Cat runs after a big
butterfly. She huffs and she
puffs, but she cannot catch it.
"Come with us to the Keep
Fit Class," says Flippy Frog.
Off they go down the lane.

They come to a big barn
and they all go inside.
"Here we are!" says Flippy.
"Now do what I do."
He gets a big ball and he
throws it up into a net.
The ball comes down on to
Flippy Frog's head . . .
BUMP!
"That is no good," says Bossy.

Flippy gets a long rope.
"Do what I do, Cuddly Cat,"
he says. "Then you will get
fit too."
But the rope is too long
and Flippy falls over it.
Down goes poor Flippy Frog . . .
BUMP!
"That is no good," says
Cuddly Cat.

Flippy runs up to a big bag.
He begins to hit it.
"Do what I do," he says to
the three little ducklings.
Flippy hits the bag, but the
bag comes back and hits him.
Down goes poor Flippy Frog . . .
BUMP!
"That is no good," says
Bossy Bear.

Paddy Dog runs by.
"Look!" he says. "I can
throw the ball and catch it."
"Look at Paddy!" say the
ducklings. "He can catch the
big ball. That is very good.
Paddy Dog is very fit."
But Flippy Frog is cross.

Cuddly Cat runs by.
"Look at me!" she says.
"I can skip, but I do not
fall down."
She can skip very fast.
"Look at Cuddly!" say the
ducklings. "That is very
good."
Cuddly runs and skips with
the rope, but she does not
fall. Flippy does not look.
Flippy Frog is very cross.

Bossy and Hoppy go up to the big bag. They begin to hit it. They are very good.

"Look at Bossy and Hoppy!" say the three little ducklings. Flippy does not look.

Flippy Frog is VERY cross.

"He IS funny," say the three little ducklings.

"He is SILLY!" says Dilly.

"I shall keep fit in my own way. Come with me."

Dilly Duck and her ducklings go back to the duck pond. Cuddly Cat and Bossy Bear go with them. Paddy Dog and Hoppy Rabbit run after them. Last of all comes poor Flippy Frog. He does not look very fit. He hops after them all the way back to the duck pond. He huffs and he puffs.

Dilly Duck is in the pond.
She swims up and down.
She does not huff and she
does not puff.
The three little ducklings
jump into the pond after her.
PLOP! PLOP! PLOP!
"This is the best way for
ducks to keep fit," says
Dilly Duck.
"It is the best way for
frogs too!" says Flippy.
PLOP!

Say these words again

flowers	butterfly
jumps	barn
own	throws
along	shall
catch	good
where	rope
push	what

What are they doing?

swimming

skipping

hitting

hopping

throwing

Who plays a trick on
Dilly Duck?
Does Paddy Dog see
a real ghost?
Who saves Hoppy's kite?
What does Bossy Bear do
at the circus?
Who pretends to be
a pirate?
What makes Flippy Frog
cross?

What are they doing?

washing

drinking

sitting

digging

sleeping